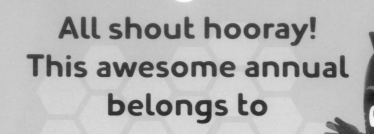

All shout hooray!
This awesome annual belongs to

....

Write your name here

ANNUAL 2018

CONTENTS

MEET THE PJ MASKS

By day, the PJ Masks are regular kids just like you and your friends.

But when night comes, EVERYTHING changes . . .

GREG

CONNOR

AMAYA

LOOK OUT, NIGHT-TIME BADDIES – THE PJ MASKS ARE COMING!

TIME TO BE A HERO!

After dark, Connor, Amaya and Greg become the PJ Masks! Grab your colouring pencils or pens and bring our heroes to life.

GREG BECOMES GEKKO!

PJ MASKS, WE'RE ON OUR WAY!

AMAYA BECOMES OWLETTE!

CONNOR BECOMES CATBOY!

INTO THE NIGHT TO SAVE THE DAY!

THE CATBOY FILES

Catboy is the leader of the PJ Masks, because he's the oldest – only by a couple of months! But that's important, right?

BY MY CAT'S WHISKERS!

PJ POWERS

- SUPER CAT SPEED
- SUPERSONIC HEARING
- SUPER CAT LEAP

10

TO THE CAT-CAR!

This is not your usual car.
OH NO.
Think of the fastest car you can.
THIS IS FASTER.
Think of the loudest car you can.
THIS IS LOUDER.

CAT-CAR FACT: THIS car fires furballs. If you see it coming, get out of the way!

CATBOY SKILLS TEST

Catboy moves FAST in the DARK
so it is tough to spot him. Look at these shadows.
Can you work out which one is an exact match
to his picture on the left?

A   B   C

The answers are on page 61.

THE OWLETTE FILES

Trouble in the city? Don't panic! Owlette is ready to swoop in and save the day. This hero is always flying high!

FLUTTERING FEATHERS!

PJ POWERS

- SUPER OWL WINGS
- OWL EYES
- OWL WING WIND

TO THE OWL GLIDER!

Owlette's amazing plane has bright lights to spot baddies hiding in the shadows. It also has claws to clutch them with!

OWL GLIDER FACT:

The Glider can loop-the-loop through the sky at amazing speed!

OWLETTE SKILLS TEST

LET'S TEST YOUR *SUPER SENSES!*
Look at all of these Owlettes. Now close your eyes and put your finger on the one in the pink box.

13

TO THE GEKKO-MOBILE!

Watch this machine glide underwater then roll like a tank on land . . . if you can spot it!

GEKKO-MOBILE FACT

This multi-terrain vehicle can stick to any surface, just like Gekko.

GEKKO SKILLS TEST

WRIGGLING REPTILES!

Where's Gekko gone? Colour in all of the shapes marked with a green dot to reveal his hiding place.

SUPER-SIGHT CHALLENGE

The PJ Masks have got a busy night ahead of them – there are villains all over this rooftop! Look at the picture, then try and answer the questions.

How many Ninjalinos can you see?

Which villain has got his arms crossed?

What colour is Romeo's coat?

16

How many lights are shining on Luna Girl's Luna-Board?

Is there a moon or a sun in the sky?

How many windows have lights shining in them?

Who is up in the sky?

17

Catboy Connections

Catboy is grappling with a puzzle.
Can you help? Grab a pencil and go!

DO draw a line to connect the matching pictures.

DON'T cross any lines that you've already made!

NIGHT-TIME BADDIES

When there's trouble, these three villains are never far away.
Want to get a good look at them?
All you have to do is join up the dots!

Now colour in the baddies.

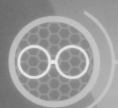

THE ROMEO FILES

Romeo may not have any super-powers, but he does have a brilliant brain. This baddie will do anything to get in the way of the PJ Masks!

YOU'VE SPOILED MY FUN THIS TIME PJ MASKS . . . BUT I'LL BE BACK!

~~POWER:~~ BRAIN POWER

~~HELPER:~~ ROBOT

~~VEHICLE:~~ ROMEO'S LAB

ROMEO'S LAB

Anything could be going on inside this spooky-looking monster machine. It's filled with screens, gadgets and ear-bending alarms!

SYMBOL SELECTOR

LAB   HOME   STAY   KEEP   AWAY   OUT

ROMEO SKILLS TEST

LET'S TEST YOUR SUPER SENSES!

Romeo has put a sign on the side of the Lab. What does it say? Use the Symbol Selector to match the right words to the pictures.

THE LUNA GIRL FILES

Luna Girl wants everything for herself – if she doesn't get her way, she is going to throw a terrible tantrum!

OOH! YOU PUNY PJ MASKS!

POWER: LUNA-MAGNET

HELPERS: MOTHS

VEHICLE: LUNA-BOARD

MOON MOTHS

When Luna Girl needs back-up, she calls up a cloud of moths! The pesky mini-spies swarm around the PJ Masks and get in their way.

LUNA GIRL SKILLS TEST

LET'S TEST YOUR SUPER SENSES!
Luna Girl is searching for her fluttering moths. Which trail will take her to the swarm?

1
2
3

THE NIGHT NINJA FILES

Night Ninja is a high-kicking, back-flipping nuisance! The villain also has an army of mini-me Ninjalinos to help him pester the PJ Masks.

I DO THE EVIL LAUGH! MWAH-HA-HA!

- **POWER:** MARTIAL ARTS
- **HELPERS:** NINJALINOS
- **VEHICLE:** JUMPING

NAUGHTY NINJALINOS

Each Ninjalino is a tiny Night Ninja mini-me! Their army always turns up when there's mischief to be made.

NIGHT NINJA SKILLS TEST

LET'S TEST YOUR *SUPER SENSES!* Night Ninja's weapon of choice is the Sticky-Splat. Who has the baddie splatted tonight? Try and guess.

WATCH OUT, PJ MASKS!

Uh-oh. Someone sneaky has tiptoed into the PJ Masks' HQ. Which villain is hiding in the shadows? Point to him quickly, before he can get up to any more mischief!

SPOTTED THE BADDIE? GOOD WORK!
Now draw a circle around the villain's name.

NIGHT NINJA   LUNA GIRL   ROMEO

Go, Go, Go!

The PJ Masks are ready for an adventure! Which super vehicle will they ride in tonight?

YOU decide! Colour in the vehicle you'd like to see in action.

27

Gekko's Super Gekko Sense

One day, Connor asks Amaya and Greg to play 'Capture the Castle'.
"Let's make two teams," he says. "Each team has a base and a flag.
The first team to capture the other team's flag and plant it on
their base is the winner!"

The friends head to the park.
"Uh, guys?" cries Amaya. "Why is there a Night Ninja flag on top of HQ?"
The game will have to wait. The PJ Masks have a job to do!

Night falls in the city. A brave band of heroes get ready
to battle fiendish villains. The PJ Masks have
to find out what Night Ninja is up to.
"Cat Ears!" says Catboy.
"I can hear Ninjalinos giggling."
"Owl Eyes!" adds Owlette.
"I can see them. They're
at our school!"

Gekko feels left out.
How come HIS super powers can't help?
"I have my... Super Gekko Sense!" he says.
"I can tell when danger is near."
Catboy and Owlette look confused.
They have never heard of that super
power before.

The heroes rush to their school. Night Ninja is standing on the roof!
"Hey!" calls Catboy. "Why did you put a flag on our HQ?"
"Because that was YOUR base, and now it is MINE," replies the
baddie. "I'm going to be the best ever at Capture the Flag!
And if you lose, I get your HQ!"

"With my Gekko sense, we're totally going to win this," laughs Gekko.
"Easy peasy, lizard squeezy!"
Catboy and Owlette are not so sure.

The PJ Masks go back to their HQ. They need to work out a game plan! "My Super Gekko Sense tells me that Night Ninja is inside the school now," says Gekko. "That means he isn't watching his flag. Let's go and grab it."

"I sense that Night Ninja went THAT way!" shouts Gekko, heading for the school. "Really?" says Catboy. "You were wrong before." He thinks they should turn back towards the HQ instead.

Catboy and Gekko creep to the school. Gekko is just about to grab the flag, when – ugghhh! – he gets pelted with sticky splats! Night Ninja had been RIGHT there the whole time. "Your Super Sense was wrong, Gekko," says Catboy.

Catboy and Owlette are worried about Gekko. They decide to leave the flag unguarded, so they can track him down. The PJ Mask has landed himself in a ton of trouble. Gekko has been splatted by Night Ninja, again!

Owlette and Catboy help Gekko get free. Suddenly the Mega Meow Alarm sounds from HQ. Night Ninja has captured the flag! "I am sorry," says Gekko. "I don't even have Super Gekko Sense. Now it's time to be a REAL hero!"

Night Ninja is just about to plant the flag, when – whoosh!
– the Owl Glider whizzes down beside him. Something
invisible swipes the flag from the villain's hand.
"Huh?"
Gekko appears out of nowhere.
"Not expecting to see ME, Night Ninja?" he says.
The heroes zoom back to HQ and plant both flags on the top.
"The PJ Masks win!"

At school the next day, Amaya and Connor lose
Greg all over again. Quick as a flash, he comes
rushing out of the bushes and steals
the flag.
"I may not have Super Gekko
Sense," he grins, "but
I can still sense
a victory!"

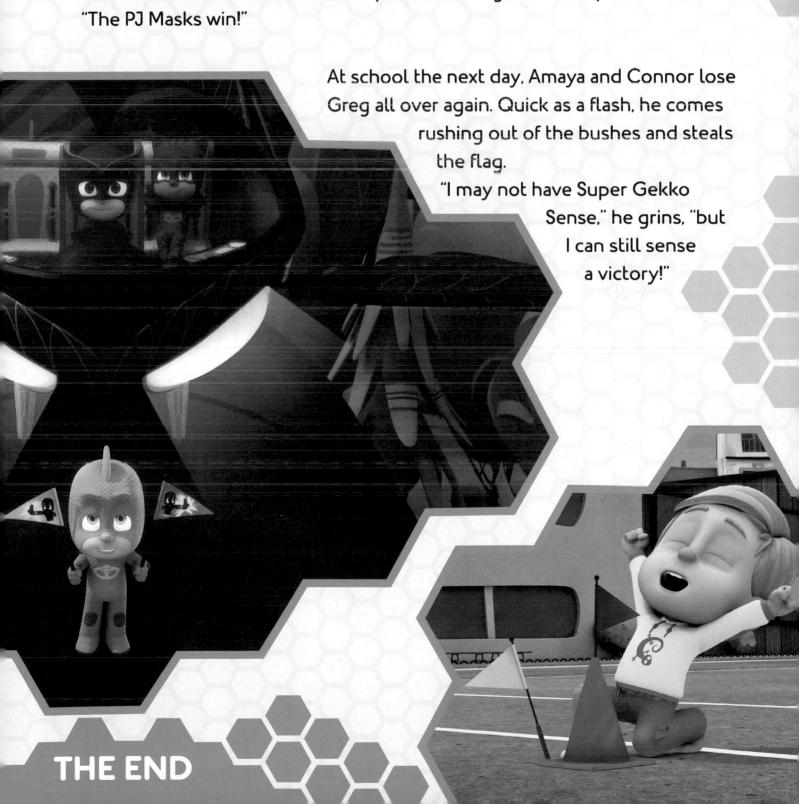

THE END

NIGHT NINJA RACE GAME

The PJ Masks need your help! Can you chase down Night Ninja and his naughty Ninjalinos? This fun board game will send you swooshing through the city.

START

1

WHAT YOU NEED:

★ Up to two friends to play with

★ A coin each to use as a counter

★ A dice

HOW TO PLAY

Take turns to throw the dice.

★

Move your counters along the board, following the instructions as you go.

★

The first player to reach the end is the winner!

Gekko has disappeared!
THROW 6 TO MOVE AGAIN.

14

13

15

16

Kidnapped by Romeo!
GO BACK TO SQUARE 11.

17

FINISH

34

2

2

3 Catboy steps in a puddle. **CAT-ASTROPHE!** **MISS A GO!**

4

5 Use a new super-power. **THROW AGAIN.**

6

Owlette spies Night Ninja up ahead. **MOVE ON 5 SQUARES.**

7

8

9

10 Grab a lift on the Owl Glider. **SLIDE ACROSS TO SQUARE 19.**

11

12

18

19

20 The Cat-Car picks you up. **ZOOM AHEAD TO SQUARE 23.**

21

22

23

24

25

26

27 Luna Girl Moth swarm! **GO BACK 3 SQUARES.**

28

FIST BUMP!

When Connor, Amaya and Greg are transforming into the PJ Masks, they touch fists and amazing things happen. Here are some new action codes to try out with your friends.

LET'S DO THIS!

GOOD JOB!

WE'RE THE BEST!

I AM READY!

SUPER SKETCHER

The PJ Masks are out patrolling the city! Who or what will the heroes find tonight? Draw in the moon, stars and the city streets.

Now colour your picture in.

TRACKER TRICK

Where has Gekko gone?
The PJ Masks need to find him fast! Find a friend, then have a go at this cool trick. All you have to do is follow the instructions at the bottom of the page.

1. Point to any picture of Catboy.

2. Move your finger left or right to the nearest picture of Owlette.

3. Move your finger straight up or down to the nearest Catboy.

4. Move your finger diagonally to the nearest Owlette.

5. Gekko will either be in the box straight above you or on your left! He's super-pleased to see you!

38

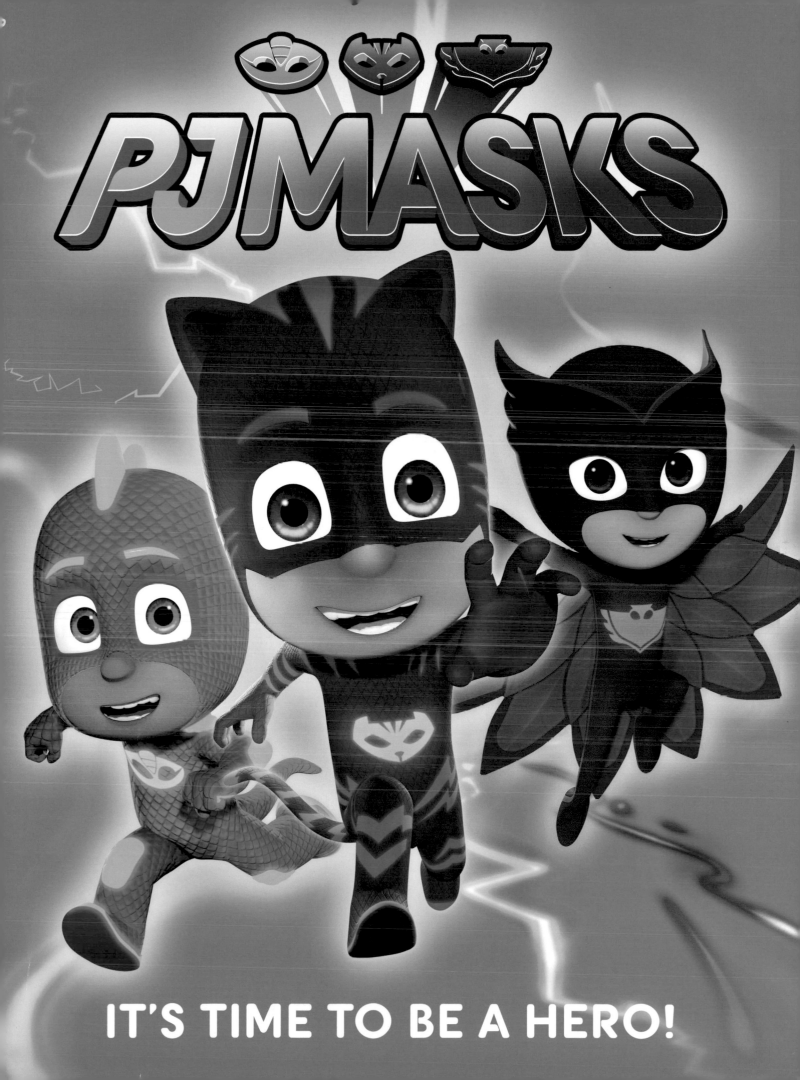

HAVE A BAD DAY!

The PJ Masks use their super-powers to see in the dark! What about you? Look carefully at these two pictures, then try to spot five differences between them.

Every time you spot a difference, colour in a star.

HQ MONSTER MAZE MYSTERY

CATBOY LEVEL

By day, the PJ Masks' HQ looks like a totem pole. By night, it becomes so much more! Put your finger at the entrance and then trace a route through the levels, all the way to the exit.

ENTRANCE

OWLETTE LEVEL

GEKKO LEVEL

CATBOY, OWLETTE AND GEKKO ARE COUNTING ON YOU

EXIT

43

MAKE YOUR OWN HQ

Would you like to make your own super HQ? Let the PJ Masks show you how!

WHAT TO DO:

Ask a grown-up to help you cut out the templates on the opposite page.

IF YOU DON'T WANT TO CUT UP YOUR BOOK, TRACE THE SHAPES ONTO A PIECE OF PAPER AND CUT THOSE OUT INSTEAD.

Stick the templates onto a thin piece of card.

Use your colouring pencils or pens to colour in each piece.

Ask your helper to cut a slit into each side of the kitchen towel tube that is about 10 cms deep.

Take the totem wings shape and slide it into the tube, so they are facing the front.

Now use glue to stick the three face templates onto the tube. Your totem is ready to display!

YOU WILL NEED:

- The totem templates on the facing page
- Scissors
- Paper glue
- Thin card
- Colouring pencils or pens
- A clean kitchen towel tube
- Ruler

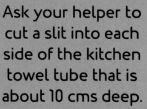

ASK A GROWN-UP TO HELP YOU WITH THIS PJ MASKS MAKE-IT. NEVER USE SCISSORS WITHOUT CHECKING FIRST.

BLAME IT ON THE TRAIN

The famous Fairground Flyer train has gone missing from the fair!
Can the PJ Masks defeat Romeo to get it back?
Use a pencil or pen to match each sentence in this story to the right picture.

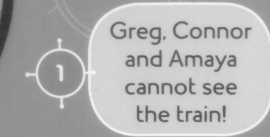

1 Greg, Connor and Amaya cannot see the train!

2 The PJ Masks all jump in the Cat-Car.

3 The heroes spot Romeo driving the train at full speed.

4 Gekko uses his super-strength to stop it in its tracks!

5 The PJ Masks return the train to the fairground.

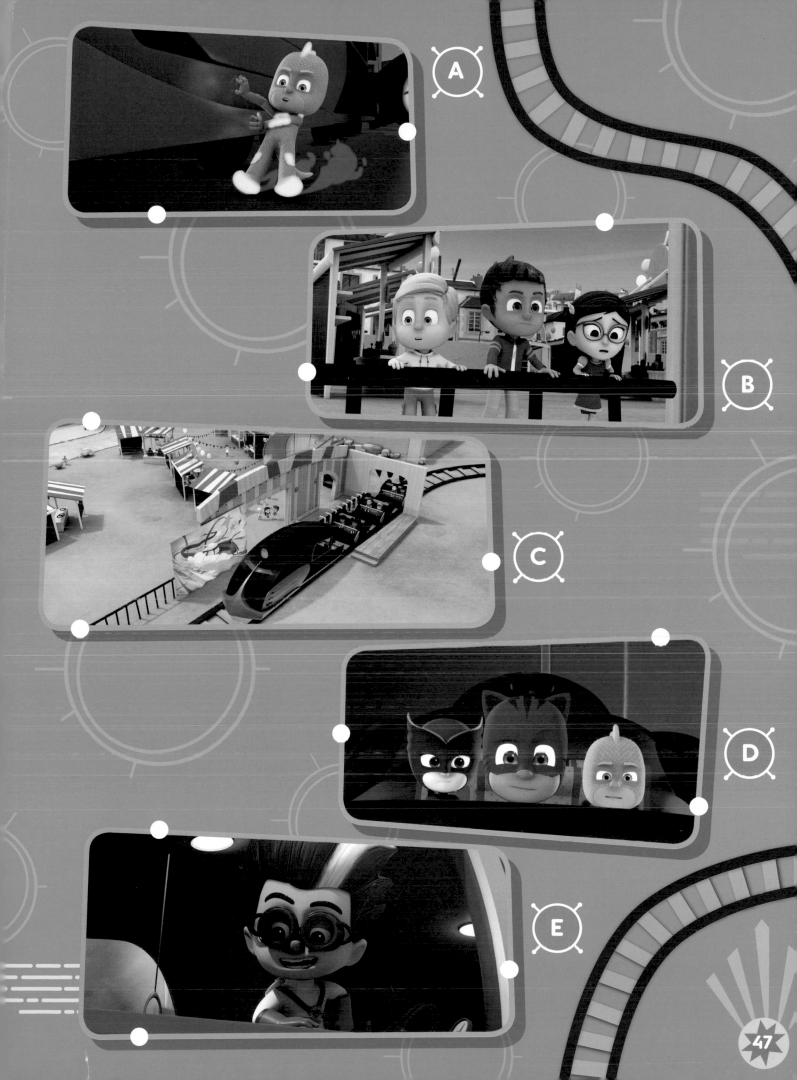

A

B

C

D

E

47

HEROES IN PYJAMAS

Which PJ Mask are you? Take this tick test to find out!
Answer the questions, then check the bottom of the page.

1 YOUR FAVOURITE COLOUR IS…
- A Green
- B Blue
- C Red

2 THERE'S A BADDIE IN THE CITY! DO YOU…
- A Stand strong and take them on
- B Use speed to chase them down
- C Think up a plan to outsmart them

3 YOU'RE IN A SUPER HURRY. DO YOU…
- A Climb over buildings
- B Take giant leaps
- C Fly

4 LUNA GIRL IS NEARBY! DO YOU…
- A Disguise yourself
- B Listen out for her
- C Watch out for her

5 IT'S TIME TO TRAVEL. WOULD YOU RATHER…
- A Whoosh along underwater
- B Race along the road
- C Glide across the sky

Mostly **A** answers
GEKKO
You are strong and a master of camouflage, just like Gekko!

Mostly **B** answers
CATBOY
You are fast and have brilliant hearing, just like Catboy!

Mostly **C** answers
OWLETTE
You are smart and have incredible eyesight, just like Owlette!

MASK MEMORIES

Greg, Connor and Amaya are planning another night-time adventure.

Look at this picture for 30 seconds.

Now turn the page over and try and see how much you can remember.

49

READY, STEADY ... GO!

If you aren't sure of the answer, take a guess.

1 What are the friends sitting on?

2 Who is wearing glasses?

3 What colour is the lamp in the background?

4 Who is sitting in the middle of the group?

5 What toy is on the shelf?

6 Who is wearing a green jumper?

ALL DONE? GOOD WORK. YOU'RE A REAL HERO!

We have to destroy this Moon-Ball. Luna Girl cannot steal any more toys!

...BUT OWLETTE HAS OTHER IDEAS. SHE JUMPS UP AND KICKS THE BALL AGAIN!

Check out my skills!

THE MOON-BALL BOUNCES ON OWLETTE. SHE GETS SUCKED INSIDE WITH ALL OF THE TOYS.

I'm so sorry. I just wanted to show how good I am at football!

CATBOY LEAPS THROUGH THE AIR AND PUSHES LUNA GIRL OUT OF THE WAY.

Super Cat Jump!

GEKKO SCRAMBLES TOWARDS THE MOON-BALL AND THEN POPS IT!

Super Gekko Muscles!

We are the best team ever!

OWLETTE IS FREE!

THE NEXT DAY, AMAYA CAN'T WAIT TO PLAY FOOTBALL WITH HER FRIENDS.

THE END

PJ PICTURES

Are you a super scribbler? Here's a fast action dice game that will put your drawing skills to the test.

How to Play

 Sit at a table with the page opposite between you, so that each player has a scene to colour in.

 Take it in turns to roll the dice. The player who throws the highest number gets to start the game.

 When it is your turn to throw, check the number on the dice against the colouring key below. Carefully colour in the part of the picture that matches the number of spots on the dice.

 Keep rolling and colouring until every part of the picture is complete. The first player to finish is the winner!

WHAT YOU NEED:

A FRIEND TO PLAY WITH

★

A DICE

★

COLOURING PENS, CRAYONS OR PENCILS

Colouring Key

 COLOUR CATBOY'S MASK

 COLOUR OWLETTE'S MASK

 COLOUR GEKKO'S MASK

 COLOUR CATBOY'S BODY

 COLOUR OWLETTE'S BODY

 COLOUR GEKKO'S BODY

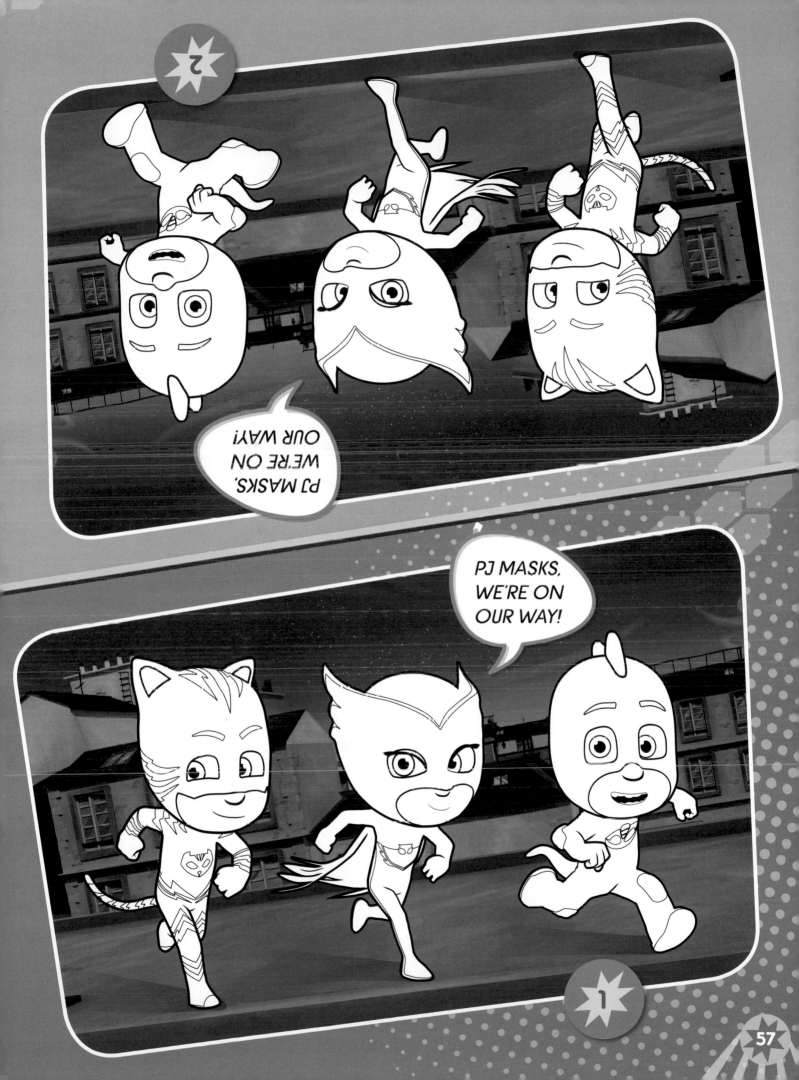

ARE YOU A PJ MASKS MASTER?

HOW WELL DO YOU KNOW THE PJ MASKS?

THIS TRUE OR FALSE QUIZ WILL TEST YOUR HERO SKILLS TO THE MAX! FIND A PEN OR PENCIL, THEN PUT A TICK NEXT TO EACH RIGHT ANSWER.

2 Owlette cannot fly.

True   False

1 During the day, the PJ Masks are just ordinary kids like you and me.

True   **False**

3 The PJ Masks' HQ is in the park.

True   False

4 Gekko is awesome at blending into his surroundings.

True   **False**

5 Catboy is super brave, but he does hate water.

True   False

58

6 The PJ Picture Player helps the PJ Masks track down villains.

True   False

7 The Cat-Car can zoom underwater.

True   False

8 Night Ninja flies around the city on the Luna-Board.

True   False

9 The Ninjalinos follow after Romeo.

True   False

10 Romeo plots to take over the world from his Lab.

True   False

THE PJ MASKS SAY...
GOOD LUCK!

PJ MASKS,
ALL SHOUT HOORAY!
'COS IN THE NIGHT,
WE SAVED THE DAY!

ANSWERS

Pages 10-11
Catboy Skills Test
C

Pages 14-15
Gekko Skills Test

Pages 16-17
Super-Sight Challenge
There are 3 Ninjalinos in the picture.
Night Ninja has got his arms crossed.
Romeo's coat is white.
Two lights are shining on Luna Girl's Luna-Board.
The moon is in the sky.
Three windows have lights shining in them.
Luna Girl is up in the sky.

Pages 24-25
Night Ninja Skills Test
Oh dear. Night Ninja has splatted one of his OWN Ninjalinos!

Pages 22-23
Luna Girl Skills Test
2

Pages 20-21
Romeo Skills Test
KEEP OUT

Page 18
Catboy Connections

Page 26
Watch out, PJ Masks!
The villain's name is Romeo.

Page 41
Street Light Spots

Pages 42-43
HQ Monster Maze Mystery

Pages 58-59
Are You a PJ Masks Master?
1. True.
2. False. Owlette is brilliant at flying.
3. True.
4. True
5. True.
6. True.
7. False. But nothing can beat it on land!
8. False. Luna Girl flies on the Luna-Board.
9. False. The Ninjalinos follow after Night Ninja.
10. True.

Page 51
Splat Party!
9

Pages 49-50
Mask Memories
1. A BED
2. AMAYA
3. GREEN
4. CONNOR
5. A ROBOT
6. GREG

Page 46-47
Blame it on the Train
1. B
2. D
3. E
4. A
5. C